KALMUS VOCAL SCORE

9175

Heinrich
PANOFKA
OP. 81

THE ART OF SINGING
TWENTY-FOUR VOCALISES

FOR ALTO, BARITONE OR BASS

Twenty-four Vocalises

For Alto, Baritone and Bass

Major Scales

H. Panofka. Op. 81, Book 1

BELWIN MILLS PUBLISHING CORP.

PRINTED IN U.S.A.

p
p
p
f
f
f
p
p
p
p
p
p
f
p
f
p
f
p

p
p
p
pp
pp
f
f
f

Minor Scales

dolce
p
dolce
p
p

f
f
f

Agility

p
f

dolce
p
dolce
p
p
p - e - cresc. - - f
p
p - e - cresc. - - f
p
p
cresc.
f
p

rit.
a tempo
calando
calando
rit.
rit.
a tempo
rit.

Agility

Andante leggiero
Baritone and Bass
Alto
4
Piano
p
p
p
a tempo
rit.
a tempo
rit.
a tempo
rit.
f

mf
cresc.
mf
cresc.
f
mf
cresc.
f
f
p
p
f
p
p
p
p
cresc.

f
f
f
p
p
p
p
p
p

f
p
f
p
f
p
f
p
f
p
p
p

Triplets

p
p
p
p
p
p
p
f
p

p
rit.
p
rit.
rit.
a tempo
p
a tempo
cre - - - - - - - - scen-
p
a tempo
p
- - - - do
f
f
f

p
p
p
rit.
p
rit.
rit.
a tempo
a tempo
a tempo
f

Triplets

p
p
p
p
p
p
f
p
f
p
f
p
p
p
f
p
3
3

f
f
f
rit.
a tempo
dim.
p
p
p

p
p
p
f
f
p
p
f
f
f
p
f
p
f
f
p

Groups of 2 Slurred Notes

p
cresc.
p
cresc.
p
cresc.
p
cresc.
p
p
p
p

rit.
a tempo
rit.
a tempo
rit.
p
p
p
f
f
f

Portamento

rit.
rit.
colla voce

Portamento

rit.
a tempo
rit.
a tempo
rit.
a tempo
rit.
p a tempo
rit.
rit.
p a tempo

Portamento

Adagio
molto espressivo e sostenuto
Baritone and Bass
p
molto espressivo e sostenuto
Alto
p
10
Piano
p
pp
cresc.

rit.
a tempo
rit.
a tempo
rit.
a tempo
cresc.
cresc.
cresc.

tremolo

Portamento

f
f
f
rit.
rit.
rit.
a tempo
p
a tempo
p
a tempo
p

p
p
rall.
rall.
rall.
a tempo
p
a tempo
p
a tempo

Portamento

rit.
f
f
rit.
f
a tempo
p
pp
p
pp
a tempo
p
pp

Twenty-four Vocalises

For Alto, Baritone and Bass

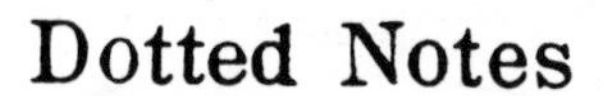

H. Panofka. Op. 81, Book II

a tempo
f
rit.
p
a tempo
f
rit.
p
f
rit.
p a tempo
p
f
p
f
f
p
f
p
p
f
p
p
f
p

f
p
f
p
f
p
f
p
f
f
p
f
p
p
f
p

Syncopation

rit.
a tempo
p
rit.
a tempo
p
p
rit.
a tempo
p
p
p
p
dim.

Legato

Allegretto
Baritone and Bass
Alto
15
Piano
p
p
p
cresc.
cresc.
cresc.
f
f
f

p
p
p
f
f
f
p
p
rit.
f
f
rit.
p
p
f
rit.

a tempo
p
a tempo
p
a tempo
p
rit.
rit.
p
p
colla voce
rit.
rit.
rit.
f

Appoggiatura, Gruppetto, Turn and Inverted Mordent

* Performed thus:

f
p
molto rit.
f
p
molto rit.
f
p
molto rit.
rit.
rit.
p
p
rit.
p
pp
rit.

Preparatory Study for the Trill

Practise at first **Lento,** then **Moderato, Allegro** and **Allegro molto**

f

p
p
p

f
f
f
f
f
f
f

Agility

cresc.
cresc.
cresc.
f
p
p
p
p
p

f
p
f
p
fp
f
p
p
p
p

f
f
f
f
f
f

p
p
p
p
p
f
f
f
3

Trills

tr
p
f

Arpeggios

Also practise staccato

pp
pp
pp

3
rit.
3
a tempo
rit.
a tempo
f
f
f

f
f
f
p
p
f
f
rit.
f
rit.

Arpeggios

Also practise staccato

dolce
dolce

p
p
p
p
f
p
f
f
f
p
p
p
f

Chromatic Scales

mf
mf
mf
f
f
f
dolce
p
dolce
p
p

f
f
f
dim.
p
p
p
cresc.
cresc.
f
f
f
p
p
p
p

f
f
f

Chromatic Scales

cresc.
pp
pp
pp
p
p
p
cresc.
ff
ff
ff

f
p
f
p
f
p
f
p
f
p
f
p
rit.
a tempo
p dolce
più lento
p dolce
più lento
rit.
a tempo
p
p
p

Tempo Iº
cresc.
cresc.
cresc.
p
p
p
f
p
p
p
p

tr
f

Intervals

cresc.
f
cresc.
f
cresc.
f
p
p
p

f
f
f
p
p
p
p
p

f
f
f
rit.
p
p
a tempo
p

p
rit.
p
rit.